HAPPY BIR

TO

....

WITH LOVE FROM

....

And Elvis

HAPPY BIRTHDAY—LOVE . . .

Complete Series

Jane Austen

Joan Crawford

Bette Davis

Liam Gallagher

Audrey Hepburn

John Lennon

Bob Marley

Marilyn Monroe

Michelle Obama

Jackie Kennedy Onassis

Elvis Presley

Keith Richards

Frank Sinatra

Elizabeth Taylor

Oscar Wilde

HAPPY BIRTHDAY
Love, Elvis

ON YOUR SPECIAL DAY

ENJOY THE WIT AND WISDOM OF

ELVIS PRESLEY

THE KING OF ROCK'N'ROLL

Edited by Jade Riley

CELEBRATION BOOKS

THIS IS A CELEBRATION BOOK

Published by Celebration Books 2023
Celebration Books is an imprint of Dean Street Press

Text & Design Copyright © 2023 Celebration Books

Cover by DSP

ISBN 978 1 915393 72 2

www.deanstreetpress.co.uk

HAPPY BIRTHDAY—LOVE, ELVIS

ELVIS Aaron Presley may have started life in a humble, two room house in Tupelo, Mississippi but by the age of 21 he was already conquering the world. Now anyone who sells 10 million records in the first year of their career has a whopper of a reason to celebrate and Elvis soon turned his triumph to what became a lifelong habit of generosity and making people happy. He gathered to himself a big group of friends and family that would become his "Memphis Mafia" and they would rent out entire movie theaters, amusement parks and even ski resorts. He gave away so many Cadillac and Lincoln cars to friends and total strangers that it became a running joke. One news reporter kidded him about doing this by saying "Hey, Elvis will you give me a car too?" And Elvis did!

Since the season of Christmas and New Year's festivities led right up to his January 8 birthday, the Graceland mansion became the setting for one long party. A certain young cousin, Billy Smith, described these extravagant soireés as "magical". With Elvis' personal cook, Mary Langston, providing a mouth-watering array of party food and punch, the fun didn't stop until the sun came up.

The actual day of Elvis' own birthday was a little quieter, as his wife Priscilla describes it. He would sit singing at the piano, his group of family and friends nearby. Pricilla states that Elvis was shy about receiving gifts and that "just your presence alone was enough for him." Perhaps birthdays were extra special for the King as he fondly looked back to his 11th birthday, when his beloved Mother, Gladys, gave him his very first guitar.

And now celebrate your own special day with the loving, tender words of wisdom from Elvis.

Elvis Presley

Ain't nowhere else in the world where you can go from driving a truck to driving a Cadillac overnight.

When you're
not in love,
you are not
alive.

Money is meant to be spread around, the more happiness it helps create, the more it's worth.

"God is love
. . . a loving
presence on all
of us.

The most beautiful thing in the world to me is a baby looking as pretty as her mama.

"

They come first . . . the most precious thing in life. A parent should do everything it takes to give a child a sense of family.

"

It's very hard
to live up to an
image, put it
that way.

Truth is like the sun.
You can shut it out
for a time, but it
ain't going away.

If you let your head get too big, it'll break your neck.

When your intelligence
don't tell you something
ain't right, your conscience
gives you a tap you on the
shoulder and says 'hold on'.
If it don't, you're a snake.

I didn't copy
my style from
anybody.

Only a dead
man's got no
reason to care.

"
Friends are
people you can talk
to . . . without words
when you have to.

"

I wasn't exactly a James Bond in Movies, but then no one ever asked Sean Connery to sing a song while dodging bullets.

Happiness is knowing that you've done a good job, whether it's professional or for another person.

I don't mind being controversial. Even Jesus wasn't loved in his day.

The child needs a helping hand or he'll grow up to be an angry young man some day.

"Don't criticize
what you don't
understand, son.
You never walked
in that man's shoes.

Death is the hardest
thing for anyone
to accept, but you
have to or you'll live
in fear of it.

If I slept with every woman the weekly magazines say I have, I would have been dead a long time ago.

The image is one thing and the human being is another . . . it's very hard to live up to an image.

When things go wrong, don't go with them.

Computers may out-think us one day, but as long as people got feelings we'll be better than they are.

Those people in
New York are not
gonna change
me none.

Values are like fingerprints. Nobody's are the same, but you leave 'em all over everything you do.

I am not the King. Jesus Christ is the King. I'm just an entertainer.

It's not how much
you have that
makes people look
up to you, it's who
you are.

My fans want my shirt. They can have my shirt. They put it on my back.

It's okay to
feel fear, just
don't show it.

Gospel music is the purest thing there is on this earth.

Animals don't hate and we're supposed to be better than them.

"
Take care of the
fans and they
will sure as hell
take care of you.

"

Never wait for tomorrow, what if tomorrow never comes?

The key to happiness
is someone to love,
something to do,
and something to
look forward to.

Do something worth remembering.

The walls have
ears, better
think before you
throw that shoe.

All I want is to know
the truth, to know
and experience God.
I'm a searcher, that's
what I'm all about.

"The army
teaches boys
to think like
men.

After a hard day
of basic training,
you could eat a
rattlesnake.

" Ambition is a dream with a V8 engine. "

It's human nature
to gripe, but I'm
going ahead
and doing the
best I can.

Adversity is sometimes hard upon a man; but for one man who can stand prosperity, there are a hundred that will stand adversity.

I'll never feel comfortable taking a strong drink, and I'll never feel easy smoking a cigarette. I just don't think those things are right for me.

Some people tap their feet, some people snap their fingers, and some people sway back and forth. I just sorta do 'em all together, I guess.

I'd just like to be treated like a regular customer.

I figure all any kid needs is hope and the feeling he or she belongs. If I could do or say anything that would give some kid that feeling, I would believe I had contributed something to the world.

Teenagers are my life and my triumph. I'd be nowhere without them.

"Whatever I will become will be what God has chosen for me."

To judge a man by his weakest link or deed is like judging the power of the ocean by one wave.

More than anything else, I want the folks back at home to think right of me.

Everybody comes
from the same source.
If you hate another
human being, you're
hating part of yourself.

"When I was a child, ladies and gentlemen, I was a dreamer. I read comic books, and I was the hero of the comic book. I saw movies, and I was the hero in the movie. So every dream I ever dreamed has come true a hundred times.

It's all a big hoax, honey. I never wrote a song in my life.

It's more important to try to surround yourself with people who can give you a little happiness.

You only pass through this life once, Jack. You don't come back for an encore.

Rock and roll is a music, and why should a music contribute to juvenile delinquency? If people are going to be juvenile delinquents, they're going to be delinquents if they hear Mother Goose rhymes.

I believe in the Bible. I
believe that all good
things come from God. I
don't believe I'd sing the
way I do if God hadn't
wanted me to.

"

I don't do
any vulgar
movements.

"

I'm not trying to be sexy. It's just my way of expressing myself when I move around.

Rhythm is something
you either have or
don't have, but when
you have it, you have
it all over.

"

Life is love and love is life.

"

There are too many
people that depend
on me. I'm too
obligated. I'm in too
far to get out.

“

The first time that I appeared on stage, it scared me to death. I really didn't know what all the yelling was about. I didn't realize that my body was moving. It's a natural thing to me. So to the manager backstage I said: 'What'd I do? What'd I do?' And he said: 'Whatever it is, go back and do it again.'

People think
you're crazy if
you talk about
things they don't
understand.

I go for all the belles, except the wedding kind.

Man, I was tame
compared to what
they do now. Are you
kidding? I didn't do
anything but just jiggle.

A lot of people seem to think I started this business. But rock'n'roll was here a long time before I came along.

We do two shows a night
for five weeks. A lotta times
we'll go upstairs and sing until
daylight—gospel songs. We
grew up with it . . . It more or
less puts your mind at ease. It
does mine.

Envy someone an'
it pulls you down.
Admire them and it
builds you up. Which
makes more sense?

"Man, I really like Vegas."

That's why I hate to get started in these jam sessions. I'm always the last one to leave.

As long as a man
has the strength
to dream, he can
redeem his soul
and fly.

Every time I think that I'm getting old, and gradually going to the grave, something else happens.

I don't know anything about music. In my line you don't have to.

"I have no use for bodyguards, but I have a very special use for two highly trained certified public accountants.

There's no job
too immense,
when you got
confidence.

The Lord can give, and the Lord can take away. I might be herding sheep next year.

Sad thing is, you can still love someone and be wrong for them.

In this day and time you can't even get sick; you are strung-out! Well by God, I'll tell you something, friend: I have never been strung-out in my life, except on music!

[On karate:] It's not just self defense, it's about . . . self control, body discipline, and mind discipline . . . and breath techniques. It involves yoga. It involves meditation. It's an art, not a sport.

I never
expected to
be anybody
important.

From the time I was
a kid, I always knew
something was going to
happen to me. Didn't
know exactly what.

I'm so lucky to be in the position to give. It's really a gift to give.

Smile. It irritates those who wish to destroy you.

Where could I go but to the Lord?

'Til we meet
again, may
God bless you.
Adios.

Elvis Presley

ABOUT THE EDITOR

Jade Riley is a writer whose interests include old movies, art history, vintage fashion and books, books, books.

Her dream is to move to London, to write like Virginia Woolf, and to meet a man like Mr. Darcy, who owns a vacation home in Greece.

61422768R00059

Wild
Planet

Contents

Wonderful Wildlife   4

The Delicate Balance   6

Upsetting the Balance

Destroying Homes   8

Alien Attack   10

The Tiger's Tale   14

Toba's Cubs   16

Wildlife Rescue

Saving Endangered Animals   18

Zoos and Parks   20

The Peace Parks of Africa   22

Living Together   24

The Wolves of Algonquin   26

The Wild Way Forward   28

Glossary   30

Index   31

Research Starters   32

Features

In the past, the sea otter was hunted for its fur. Now it faces an even greater danger. Find out what that danger is in **Coastal Waters** on page 9.

Why were cane toads introduced into Australia in the 1930s? Read **Overrun by Toads** on page 11 and decide what you think about introducing non-native animals into new countries.

Read the diary notes of a conservationist who observed a mother tiger and her cubs for eight months in **Toba's Cubs** on page 16.

What can you do to help save animals that are in danger of becoming extinct? Read **Adopt a Manatee** on page 19.

Why are some frogs endangered?

Visit www.rigbyinfoquest.com
for more about ENDANGERED ANIMALS.

Wonderful Wildlife

We share this planet with a wonderful variety of wildlife. Plants and animals live everywhere on Earth, from the hottest deserts to the deepest oceans. Scientists are not even sure how many species exist, but they do know that many are **endangered.** This means that we might lose them forever.

Species such as the dinosaur, the dodo, and the passenger pigeon are already extinct. Some species died out through natural causes. However, many species today are endangered because of people's activities. Giant pandas and blue whales are just two of the world's many endangered species.

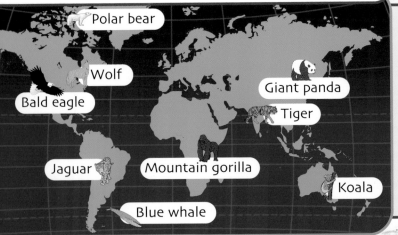

Some Endangered or Threatened Species

Polar bear

Wolf

Giant panda

Bald eagle

Tiger

Jaguar

Mountain gorilla

Koala

Blue whale

More than 100 animal species including insec and tiny anim life, disappear from Earth da A species is sa to be extinct i has not been for fifty years.

4

Dinosaurs became extinct due to natural causes. Some scientists think dinosaurs died out when a meteorite hit Earth. Smoke blocked the sun, and dinosaurs died from the cold.

The Delicate Balance

Every plant and animal on Earth has its own special home area, called its **habitat.** Different plants and animals live together and share the same habitat. They depend on each other for survival. Each of these habitats, with its life forms, is called an **ecosystem.**

A coral reef is an ecosystem. Coral reefs are limestone formations that are made up of millions of tiny animals. They provide food and shelter for fish and other sea creatures. However, people are harming the reefs by polluting them with waste products and by breaking the coral. If coral reefs die, many of the creatures that depend on them will die also.

Coral reefs are called the rain forests of the sea. They are home to more species of marine life than any other part of the ocean.

Food Chains

The plants and animals in an ecosystem are linked together in a food chain. Tiny plants called plankton are the start of an ocean food chain. They are eaten by very small animals, which in turn are eaten by larger animals. If something happens to one kind of animal or plant in the chain, all the others in the chain are affected, too.

Sometimes food chains don't work quite the way you might expect. Sun coral looks like a plant, but it is actually an animal that belongs to the same group of water animals as sea anemones and jellyfish. Like these animals, sun coral captures food by spreading its tentacles and dragging the prey into its mouth. Here, it is catching a silverside fish.

Upsetting the Balance

Destroying Homes

Most plants and animals are specially **adapted** to living in a specific habitat and cannot survive elsewhere. Sometimes people destroy or change a habitat. As the human population has grown, more and more land has been used for farming, factories, roads, and cities. Often, wildlife has been driven out and made homeless.

People have also damaged habitats by polluting land, rivers, and oceans with trash, waste products, and chemicals. Gases and fumes from factories and cars pollute the air. Without clean air, land, and water, many species have died.

Many different species, such as the spider monkeys shown here, live in the Amazon Basin. Their home is threatened by people cutting down trees and clearing land for farming. In some parts of the Amazon Basin, spider monkeys have been hunted to extinction.

Coastal Waters

Coastal waters are home to a variety of wildlife, but they are often polluted by trash and waste products.

The southern sea otter was hunted nearly to extinction for its fur. Now its greatest threat comes from oil spills. Oil damages sea otters' fur, causing them to get cold and die. There are now fewer than 2,000 southern sea otters living on the West Coast of the United States.

Southern sea otter

Alien Attack

People have also upset the balance of nature by moving animals and plants around the world. The introduction of **alien**, or **exotic**, species into areas has threatened native wildlife. A new species may prey on a native species, eat its food, or bring disease. The native species often has no natural defense against this kind of invader. The alien species may quickly spread because it has no natural enemies.

On many islands, native species became endangered when immigrants began arriving by ship. They brought cats, rats, and other predators with them. In some countries, people purposely introduced alien species to destroy pests, and these species became pests themselves.

Guam

Hawaii

Pacific Ocean

Brown tree snake

WHAT'S YOUR OPINION?

Overrun by Toads

The first cane toads were introduced into Australia in 1935. They were brought from Venezuela to help control the beetles that attacked sugarcane crops. The toads wouldn't eat the beetles, but they ate just about anything else. Today, millions of toads threaten native animals throughout Australia. What do you think about introducing non-native animals to new countries? What controls should be in place before doing this?

Aliens by Accident

Sometimes animals are introduced into new countries by accident. Brown tree snakes from southern Pacific countries traveled, probably on ships, to Guam in the northern Pacific Ocean. In Guam, brown tree snakes have killed off more than fifteen native species of birds and lizards. Hawaiian customs inspectors now fear this will happen on their islands. They must carefully search ships and airplanes for the snakes. Any snakes found have to be destroyed.

IN FOCUS

In New Zealand, many birds are flightless because they once had no natural predators. Then European immigrants arrived, bringing cats, dogs, and rats with them. These animals hunted the native birds, their chicks, and their eggs. Now many native birds are endangered, including the kakapo, the world's most unusual parrot. When frightened, the kakapo freezes on the spot, making it easy prey.

Kakapo chick— age 82 days

The last eighty-six kakapo remaining in New Zealand are carefully tracked by conservationists. They live on two small predator-free offshore islands. Up to 100 volunteer workers guard ne and feed the birds. In 2002, twenty-four chicks survived. Volunteers used specially-desi electric blankets a video equipment to keep the eggs and chicks warm and safe.

Adult kakapo

In the 1960s, the American bald eagle was threatened with extinction because of pesticide use in its habitat. Luckily, people took action. By 1994, the number of bald eagles had increased so much that they were no longer considered endangered. They are still considered threatened, however, and are protected by the Endangered Species Act.

About the Kakapo

- The kakapo is flightless and nocturnal; its name in Maori means "parrot of the night."
- It's the world's largest parrot, weighing up to 9 pounds.
- It has soft green and yellow feathers for hiding, its main form of defense.
- In times of danger, it freezes on the spot.
- It's good at climbing trees.
- It mainly eats roots, leaves, and fruit.
- The males make a strange booming call which can travel up to 3 miles.

The Tiger's Tale

The magnificent tiger is one of the world's most endangered species. At the start of the twentieth century, about 100,000 tigers roamed Asia. Today, there are fewer than 7,000. Loss of habitat, hunting, and illegal trading have all harmed the tiger.

The tiger has become a symbol of conservation efforts. Many people are working to save the species. Special wildlife areas in Asia have been set aside for tigers. Local people patrol the reserves, keeping an eye out for **poachers.** There are heavy fines for those caught trading tigers or tiger goods.

SITESEEING · PLANTS & ANIMALS ·

Why are some frogs endangered?

Visit **www.rigbyinfoquest.com**
for more about **ENDANGERED ANIMALS.**

14

White tigers may look different from most tigers, but they are not a different species. They are just white in color with blue eyes and a pink nose. White tigers are very rare in the wild. There are, however, more than 100 in the world's zoos. All these tigers are related to one white tiger that was caught in the 1950s.

Some people hunt and kill tigers just to hang heads and skins on trophy walls.

Toba's Cubs

monday, March 4
I watched Toba stalking a deer today. Her stripes blend in so well with the tall grasses that the deer didn't see her sneaking up. She leaped on its back and killed it with one bite. She then dragged the carcass off. I'm sure she's feeding cubs.

Wednesday, march 20
I have seen Toba's den. Two cubs were playing outside as Toba looked on. She spen an hour grooming them before gently carrying them by the scruff of their necks back to the safety of the den.

monday, June 10
The cubs are about six months old now. Toba took them out hunting this morning. She frightened rabbits out of the bush for them to pounce on. Afterward, the three went down to the river to cool off.

day, July 19
a met a large male on her home range today. Usually they would lick
d greet each other, but this time she growled because her cubs were nearby.
snarled back but then left her alone.

Wednesday, October 9
I haven't seen Toba for days. The cubs are hungry and calling for her.
I'm worried something has happened because poachers have been seen in
the area. The cubs can't survive without her. They won't be able to hunt on
their own until they are at least 18 months old.

Tuesday, October 15
There's still no sign of Toba. The cubs are getting weaker. We have no choice
but to take them to our permanent camp and raise them there. Hopefully,
we can release them back into the wild when they are older.

Wildlife Rescue

Saving Endangered Animals

Many conservation groups around the world work to save endangered wildlife. Organizations such as Friends of the Earth and Greenpeace help educate people about the problems facing many species. Most countries now have laws to protect endangered species and their habitats. These countries set up national parks and reserves for wildlife.

There are many things that we can do, too. We can adopt an endangered species living near our homes and find out how we can help protect it. This could include cleaning up a river or park where it lives or raising money to help with its protection.

Some whale species have been hunted almost to extinction. Members of Greenpeace often try to stop this activity by disrupting whalers on large whaling ships.

Adopt a Manatee

Manatees are unusual marine mammals that graze on seaweed and river plants. They are big, peaceful, and playful creatures. The Florida coast of the United States is home to about 3,000 manatees. They are protected by the Endangered Species Act, but they are sometimes killed accidentally by boats. They also suffer from habitat loss and pollution. Many people are helping by "adopting" a manatee and donating money for rescue projects. In return, they receive an adoption certificate, photo, and life story of "their" manatee.

MANATEE ADOPTION CERTIFICATE

Your Adopted Manatee

This is to certify that

Sarah Davies

adopted a manatee.

Signed: *R. Robertson.* Head of Manatee Protection

Zoos and Parks

Today, most modern zoos have large areas where wild animals can roam in natural surroundings. Some zoos are "open zoos." This means that some animals are kept in large, natural environments, separated from visitors only by dry or wet moats. For example, some zoos use a water moat for spider monkeys. Although the monkeys are able to swing across water, they don't because the water frightens them.

Zoos and wildlife parks educate and inspire people to care about conservation. Many zoos keep endangered animals and release their offspring back into the wild.

Spider monkey

Moat

The monkeys are separated from visitors at the zoo only by a water moat.

Helping Orphans

Sometimes wild baby animals are orphaned. They may be sent to a zoo or wildlife park to be raised by trained zookeepers.

Some are later released, but others may never be able to care for themselves in the wild. Zoos and wildlife parks provide a safe home in which these animals can live.

The Peace Parks of Africa

Nelson Mandela, formerly President of South Africa, has been a nature lover ever since he was a boy growing up alongside the great Mbashe River. Recently, he began to support the Peace Parks Foundation. The foundation aims to create a series of "peace parks," or conservation areas, that cross national borders. Wild animals can move from park to park, and from country to country, in safety. The new parks include local communities in conservation efforts, provide jobs, and help encourage peace between different nations.

Nelson Mandela

Crossing Borders

Kgalagadi Transfrontier Park became the world's first "peace park" when it was opened in 2000. The new park joined the Gemsbok National Park in Botswana with the Kalahari Gemsbok National Park in South Africa. Animals and tourists now move freely between these two countries.

The newest park is the Great Limpopo Transfrontier Park which spreads across three international borders—South Africa's, Zimbabwe's, and Mozambique's. New activities such as bird-watching, lake cruises, and four-wheel drive tours will attract tourists to the park. The park covers more than 21,000 square miles of land.

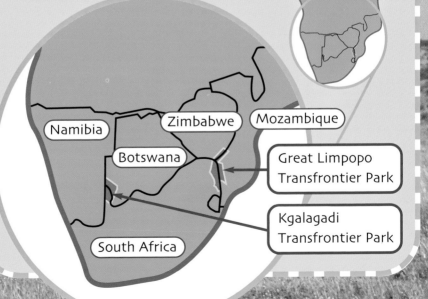

AFRICA

Namibia

Zimbabwe

Mozambique

Botswana

Great Limpopo Transfrontier Park

Kgalagadi Transfrontier Park

South Africa

Living Together

Sometimes it's difficult to balance the needs of wildlife with the needs of people. Many endangered species are found in countries where people are very poor. They may poach rare animals to feed their families, or they may clear the land to farm. They may kill wild animals to protect their crops and livestock.

There are ways, however, that people and wildlife can learn to live together. For example, local communities can benefit from conservation. National parks attract ecotourists—people who pay to see wildlife in their natural habitat. This brings money into the communities and creates jobs.

WHAT'S YOUR OPINION?

In some African countries, local farmers are unhappy about forming national parks because it means they can no longer farm their land. Some people are also unhappy about sharing their land with wild animals that can destroy their crops. The aim of many governments, however, is to show local communities that they can earn a living from working with wildlife. Before wildlife parks are established though, governments must talk with local people to make sure they are happy about the changes in their area.

What do you think about forming national parks? Should local farmers lose their land? Should the wildlife be free to move between countries?

The role of park ranger is just one of the jobs created when national parks are formed.

The Wolves of Algonquin

Wildlife parks are sometimes the last **refuge** for many species. In Canada, Algonquin Park is home to the endangered Eastern wolf. For centuries, people have feared wolves and hunted them. The wolves of Algonquin, however, have been protected since the park opened in 1893. The 3,000-square-mile park is also home to moose, deer, and beavers, which are wolves' prey.

A decade ago, scientists noticed that the population of park wolves was falling. The problem was hunting and trapping outside the park. In 2001, the Ontario government announced a ban on the hunting and trapping of wolves in areas surrounding the park.

The Eastern Wolf

The Eastern wolf is closely related to the endangered red wolf of the United States. Eastern wolves live mainly in the Great Lakes and St. Lawrence regions of Quebec and Ontario. Their largest protected habitat is Algonquin Park. It is home to about 170 wolves. Across the wolves' entire range, only about 2,000 remain.

Cry Wolf!

On August evenings, more than 2,000 people gather at Algonquin Park to join in a "Public Wolf Howl." Led by park staff, people imitate the howls of wolves and listen in wonder as the wolves howl back! This strange sound has haunted people for centuries, but as park staff explain, more than 60,000 people travel within the park every year and nobody has ever been attacked by a wolf.

The Wild Way Forward

People of the world need to work together to help save endangered wildlife. Every species on Earth is part of the web of life. If we damage one part of the web, we can damage it all.

In 1992, world leaders met at an **Earth Summit**. They discussed how countries could act together to save endangered wildlife and their habitats. Many countries drew up action plans to protect and preserve their wildlife and the environment. Since then, countries have met regularly to discuss conservation issues. They sometimes disagree on the best way forward, but they all agree that action is needed to save our wild planet.

Children were an important part of the Earth Summit held in Brazil in 1992.

Discussing the Environment

The International Children's Conference on the Environment has been held every two years since 1995. It is part of the United Nations Environment Program. Some of the main goals for the children attending these conferences are:

- to increase understanding of the environment,
- to meet other children from around the world,
- to talk about their concerns for the environment and share information about what they are doing in their communities to help.

Opening ceremony, International Children's Conference on the Environment, 2002

29

Glossary

adapt – change and adjust to fit with the conditions in the surrounding environment. Once an animal or plant has adapted to its environment, any changes in that environment make survival difficult.

alien – belonging to another country. If an animal is described as being an alien in a country, it means that it is not a native and has been brought in from another country.

Earth Summit – a meeting in which world leaders discuss the environmental, social, and economic issues affecting the international community. Issues discussed at past Earth Summit meetings include climate change, human rights, and careful management of Earth's resources.

ecosystem – a community of plants and animals and the environment in which they live

endangered – a species that is in danger of becoming extinct. A species can also be described as being threatened. This means it is likely to become endangered in the near future, especially if some of the conditions in its environment are not changed.

exotic – from a faraway country

habitat – the place and natural conditions in which plants and animals live

poach – to take animals from someone else's land without permission. Poachers usually take animals to sell them.

refuge – a place that provides protection and shelter for animals that have nowhere else to go

Index

American bald eagles   13

cane toads   11

dinosaurs   4–5

Earth Summit   28

endangered species   4, 9–10, 12–20, 24, 26–27

extinct species   4–5

food chains   7

Great Limpopo Transfrontier Park   23

habitats   6, 8–9, 13, 18–19, 24

International Children's Conference   29

introduced species   10–12

kakapo   12–13

Kgalagadi Transfrontier Park   23

manatees   19

Mandela, Nelson   22

sea otters   9

spider monkeys   8–9, 20–21

tigers   14–17

wildlife parks   18, 21–27

wolves   26–27

zoos   20–21

Research Starters

1 Find out about some animals that have been introduced into your country. Why were they introduced? Have they caused any problems for your country's native animals?

2 Read about "adopting" manatees on page 19. Then find out what other endangered animals you can adopt. If you could choose to adopt one of these animals, which one would it be? Is there anything else you could do to help this animal?

3 Scientists have found more than 1 million different species on Earth, but they think there may be as many as 30 million. In which of Earth's habitats do you think scientists might find more species?

4 Choose a native animal that lives near your home. Make a food chain that includes this animal. Are there any environmental factors that affect this animal or any other plant or animal in the food chain? Make a list of problems that may affect the plants or animals in this food chain during the future.